Contents

The door

Go and open the door.
  Maybe outside there's
  a tree, or a wood,
  a garden,
  or a magic city.

Go and open the door.
  Maybe a dog's rummaging.
  Maybe you'll see a face,
or an eye,
or the picture
        of a picture.

Go and open the door.
  If there's a fog
  it will clear.

Go and open the door.
  Even if there's only
  the darkness ticking,
  even if there's only
  the hollow wind,
  even if
      nothing
        is there,
  go and open the door.

At least
there'll be
a draught.

Miroslav Holub
translated by Ian Miller

The White Horse of Uffington

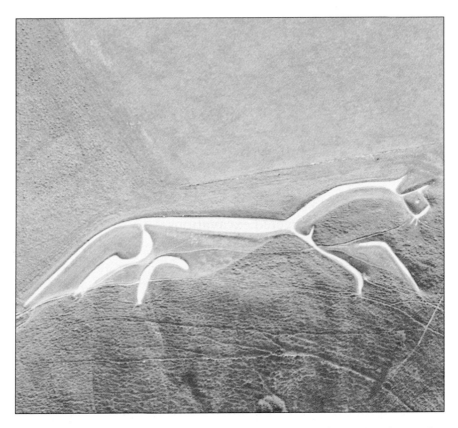

Galloping across the south Oxfordshire downland is the stylized figure of a horse. It has recently been shown to be the oldest hill figure in Britain, more than 1000 years older than anyone had believed. The White Horse of Uffington was first recorded in the twelfth century as one of the "Wonders of Britain", along with other mysteries such as Stonehenge and the Rollright Stones.

Arguments have raged for hundreds of years about the figure's age and purpose. Many historians believed it was Anglo-Saxon in origin. Others suggested it might have an earlier Celtic origin, because of the similarity of the stylized "beaked" design to those found on Iron Age coins. Now a new archaeological investigation of the Horse and the surrounding landscape has shown that it is, in fact, even older. It belongs to the late Bronze Age, between 1400 and 600 BC.

The investigation was carried out by the Oxford Archaeological Unit (OAU) at the behest of the National Trust, which owns and manages the site, and English Heritage, which takes a "guardianship" role over this ancient monument. David Miles and Simon Palmer led the investigation, which involved initial geophysical surveys, computerized aerial mapping and ground surveys, and was followed by small targeted excavations.

The Horse was thought to be no more than an etching into the surface of the hillside, reinforced by generations of "scourings". But recently-discovered section drawings from a little-known 1940s excavation by W.F. Grimes showed that the figure consists of deep, chalk-filled trenches. The Oxford Archaeological Unit was able to excavate sections of the beak and body and take soil samples from the most deeply buried strata. The Oxford Archaeological Research Laboratory used a revolutionary new technique known as Optical Stimulated Luminescence Dating to find out when these buried soils were last exposed to sunlight – in other words, when the figure was first cut.

The Bronze Age White Horse, set in its commanding position above the Vale, can only have been maintained because it was revered as a sacred place throughout its long history – first as a burial site, later as a pagan symbol in Anglo-Saxon myth and finally as a Christianised adaptation to the newer mythology of St George and the Dragon. It remains one of the most evocative symbols of Britain's past and still one of the most mysterious.

ANGLO-SAXON RIDDLES

The wave, over the wave, a weird thing I saw,
through-wrought, and wonderfully ornate:
a wonder on the wave – water became bone.

1

I am puff-breasted, proud-crested,
a head I have, and a high tail,
eyes and ears and one foot,
both my sides, a back that's hollow,
a very stout beak, a steeple neck
and a home above men.

        Harsh are my sufferings
when that which makes the forest tremble
        takes and shakes me.
Here I stand under streaming rain
and blinding sleet, stoned by hail;
freezes the frost and falls the snow
on me stuck-bellied. And I stick it all out
for I cannot change the chance that made me.

2

(Answers on inside back cover.)

Bug Muldoon

The sun began to slide over the horizon in disgust. I knew how it felt. It had been a long day, and it wasn't over yet. I felt like I had covered the entire Garden ten times over. I had. My legs were aching – all six of them – and I was getting awful tired of this case. I just wanted to crawl under a rock someplace. Still, an insect's gotta do what an insect's gotta do, especially when he's being paid.

The name's Muldoon – Bug Muldoon. I'm a sleuth – a private investigator, if you want the full title. I'm the best sleuth in the whole Garden, not to mention the cheapest. Fact is, I'm just about the *only* sleuth for hire in the Garden. The only one still alive, that is.

I was working a missing-insect case. It was nothing special, but in my line of work you take whatever you're offered. It pays the rent.

I had been sitting around in my office that morning, wondering what to do. I had just finished a big case out of town, but now I was back and looking for work. A beetle has to eat, you know? Things were so slow I was even starting to think that I should give the place a spring clean. I was still thinking about it an hour later, when I saw potential clients – three earwigs crawling up by the flower beds. I was curious – you don't see many earwigs down this end of the Garden. They tend to stay up by the garbage cans near the House, the exclusive end of the Garden.

They mooched around nervously by a clump of grass for a while, whispering to each other. Me, I just waited. When they had worked up enough courage, they approached my office, which is a patch of soil underneath a rose bush. They slid their slender brown bodies through the weeds that form my front door. The biggest of the three spoke.

"Mr Muldoon?" he asked.

"Bug. The name is Bug." (It makes me tense when people call me Mister.) "What do you guys want?"

The big one introduced himself as Larry. Nice name, I thought. Larry did all the talking. The other two nodded their heads in encouragement.

"It's our brother, Eddie," said Larry. "He's gone missing..." The other two jiggled their heads.

They needn't have bothered – this sounded like a story I'd heard a zillion times before. A bug going missing isn't exactly big news in the Garden. Still, the three earwigs looked like they expected me to ask some questions, so I did. Anything to oblige a client.

"When did he disappear?" I asked. It seemed like as good a place to start as any.

Larry's antennae waved nervously as he spoke. He was an edgy kinda guy.

"Late last night was the last time we saw him..."

"And did he say anything – any indication that he was going somewhere?"

Larry hesitated. It gave one of the other two a chance to chip in.

"He said he was going to the meadow!" he blurted.

Larry shook his head. "Eddie was always talking about taking off for the meadow some day. That's all it was – talk. It didn't mean anything... Eddie was all talk, he'd never really do it –"

I nodded, but I knew better. How many innocent young insects had I met who dreamed of a better life outside of this Garden – in the meadow on the other side of the stream? They thought that life would be easier. They thought they could spend their days there without always worrying about being eaten by a spider, a bird, or just by the bug next door. Now, I like fairy stories as much as the next beetle, but I knew one thing: life was as hard in the meadow as it was in this hellhole of a Garden that we call home. If Eddie had struck out for the meadow, there was no guarantee he had made it. Still, I didn't see any point in turning away clients.

"Could be he headed for the meadow, could be he got stuck along the way. If the second is true, I might be able to find him," I said.

I told them that I would look for Eddie, or at least try to dig up any information on where he had gone. I told them my daily fee – plus expenses – and they didn't look too worried.

Before they left, Larry leaned forward.

"One thing Mr – one thing, Bug," he said. His voice was low so his little brothers could not hear. "Eddie runs around with a rough crowd. A lot of his friends are wasps. But he's a good kid at heart..."

"I'll do what I can, Larry," I said. "If I find anything out, where can I contact you?"

Larry looked me straight in the eye. "We have a little place near the dustbins. We'll be there."

And then they were off, scurrying into the grass like a trio of amber torpedoes.

And so I had spent the whole day tramping all over the Garden – trying to find out what happened to Eddie the earwig.

I started out asking questions around the patio. No one I spoke to could give me much information. I ran into a bunch of young earwigs who told me that Eddie had thought he was a bigshot – always sounding off about leaving the Garden.

Near the trash cans I spoke to a skinny-legged crane-fly who told me that Eddie the earwig was a bug just looking for trouble, and he hoped that he had found it. He wouldn't say any more than that, but suggested that I talk to Eddie's friends, the wasps.

I thanked him politely but decided not to take his advice – in this Garden you don't approach the wasps if you can help it. Not unless you want to be stung to death. Personally, I don't.

I didn't have any leads yet, but I was starting to form a picture of the missing bug. I guessed Larry had been right – brother Eddie had been the kind of insect just itching to get out of the Garden.

I decided to concentrate my efforts on the East Side – the direction the meadow lay in. I questioned whoever I ran into, but no one had spotted Eddie. Worms, beetles, flies – they all came up empty. I was getting fed up. Surely *someone* must have seen him?

I widened my search, heading down further south. Hour after hour I trudged across grass, soil, concrete, and grass again. As the day crept by, I began to think that something strange was going on in the Garden. I couldn't put a feeler on it, but it was somehow different from when I'd left. There was a new tension in the air – the kind of feeling you get when a storm is about to break and you can feel it in your guts – trouble on the way. All the bugs I spoke to seemed edgier, more defensive.

When I told a shield-bug that I was looking for a missing earwig, he answered, "So what? Tell me who isn't missing nowadays." Then he scurried off on his business.

That's the way the whole day went. After speaking to dozens of insects, I had made no progress – not a single clue about what had happened to Eddie the earwig. And then I ran into Jake...

He spotted me from above and buzzed down to land on a sod of turf in front of me. Jake is a housefly. He's also a sugar addict, owing to the fact that he once landed in a bowl of sugar cubes. Now he couldn't get enough of the stuff. And when he *didn't* get his sugar fix, he began to quiver and shake, which is why some bugs know him as Shaky Jake. Personally, I think nicknames like that are impolite.

"How's it going, Shaky?" I said.

"P-p-pretty good, B-Bug," managed Shaky Jake. His compound eyes flitted this way and that, and he skittered sideways. I guessed he hadn't had any sugar for a while.

"Still got the sweet tooth?" I asked.

"S-s-still got it." Then he added. "Not s-s-seen you for a while, B-Bug?"

"Been away on a case," I answered. OK – that was the small talk done with. Now down to business.

"Hey, Jake," I said, "I need some information."

"Got a new c-case, Bug?"

I nodded. Jake sometimes supplied me with information, and in return I did him a favour every so often. It was a system that suited us pretty well.

"I'm looking for an earwig, name of Eddie. Young guy – ran with a bad crowd, made a lot of big talk about striking out for the meadow..."

Jake thought for a moment. "I heard an earwig was seen d-down by the compost heap this morning, down by the... the..."

He couldn't bring himself to say the word. I guess he thought even saying the name might jinx him in some way. I helped out.

"Down by the spider?"

Shaky Jake nodded nervously.

"Did he get away?"

Even as I asked the question, I knew it was stupid: the spider down by the compost heap was enormous. Once you were in his neighbourhood, "getting away" was no longer a consideration.

So... the mystery was solved – Eddie had ended up as a light snack for the spider. Telling Larry and the boys wouldn't be easy. But before I did that, the least I could do was go check out the story for myself. Just to be sure.

I turned to go. "Thanks for the info, Jake," I said. "Go find yourself a piece of candy."

"H-hey, Bug!" Shaky Jake called after me. "You be c-c-careful out there."

"Don't worry, Jake, I've got no intention of providing the second course."

I headed south.

The web was huge. It was fixed to an old oil-can on one side and a rake that leant against the compost heap on the other. In a way it was beautiful – the way the fading sunlight caught its strands – but it wasn't quite so beautiful when you remembered what it was for. How many insects had gone to their deaths inside its delicate patterns, I wondered.

I kept a safe distance. The spider sat motionless at the side of the web. It was gigantic. It looked like it should be in the Amazon rain forest, not at the bottom of some back garden.

And there, suspended in the centre of the web, were the remains of Eddie. Or at least I guessed that's what it was, I couldn't be sure. The body had been wrapped up in the spider's thread, and half of it had been eaten already. It wasn't a pretty sight.

A light breeze blew. The web swayed, but the spider didn't stir. I felt like I should say something.

"So long, Eddie," I said, though no one was there to hear. Then I turned around and began the long journey up to the dustbins.

No more school?

In the spring, between Easter and half term, Kevin Barnes began to wish more than anything that he didn't have to go to school.

Kevin was a first-year in his local comprehensive, and for most of that year he hadn't minded school at all. But that spring everything changed. For Kevin, school became a place to keep away from. Not because he was bored or anything, but because he was *frightened* – by something only he knew about.

It had started one day before Easter, when Kevin was staring out of the classroom window. He was looking at a big tree just beyond the fence round the schoolyard. It was a half-dead sycamore that had been blasted during the winter by a windstorm *and* a bolt of lightning, at the same time. Or so people said. It was leaning halfway over, with some of its roots torn up, and Kevin had heard that it was soon to be chopped down because it was dangerous.

That would be something to watch from the window, he thought idly. And then, as he gazed at the tree, the sunlight hit something, at just the right angle, under the torn-up roots of the tree. It was something bright, catching Kevin's gaze, glinting like shiny glass or metal.

When it was time for break, he went out to investigate. The fence around the school playground was made of straight-up-and-down iron bars with sharp points on top, like the bars of a cage for animals. The bars were far enough apart to let some of the smaller first-years squeeze between them. They weren't supposed to do it, but they often did.

So Kevin squeezed through and went over to the tree.

"Where you going, Kev?" called one of his friends.

"You bunking off?" called another.

Paying no attention to them, Kevin stooped down and peered at the loose earth under the tree's torn-up roots. And there it was, the shiny thing that he had seen. Picking it up, he was pleased to see that it was much more interesting than broken glass or the lid of a tin. It was a metal object, very shiny and perfectly smooth, about the shape and size of a small egg.

Kevin had no idea what it could be. Then a weird idea came to him – that it was a mini-spaceship from another world, which had arrived with the lightning bolt that had blasted the tree. He smiled to himself, imagining the metal egg to be full of tiny green aliens, each about the size of a pinhead. As he smiled, he was turning the thing over in his hands, feeling its smooth shininess, rubbing and squeezing and twisting it.

And as he twisted it, it came open.

It fell apart in two bits, one bigger than the other. And there was something inside the bigger bit. Kevin shook it out into his hand and saw that it looked like a strange sort of *insect* – brown and shiny, curled up like a woodlouse and about the same size.

At that moment, it came alive. Its body uncurled, showing that its front half was thin and flat, with a tiny narrow head, while its back half was a bit larger and bulgier. On its head, a pair of feelers lifted up and began to wave around. And it seemed to have a great many short legs, as thin as hairs.

Suddenly the legs carried it in a fast scuttling run up over Kevin's wrist and on to his sleeve. Kevin was so startled that he nearly dropped the two parts of the metal egg. But at least the weird bug didn't seem to be the biting or stinging sort. And Kevin smiled again when the bug stopped its scuttling run and sat still on his sleeve, waving its feelers.

"Kev! Teacher's coming!"

It was his friend's voice, warning him. Looking up, he saw a teacher – on playground duty – walking slowly towards the fence. She hadn't seen Kevin, so he quickly scooped the bug back into the metal egg and tried to fit the two parts back together, while hurrying to the fence. He was startled again when the two parts went together easily and stayed together. And not the slightest mark showed on the smooth metal, where they had been joined.

Then Kevin slid the thing into his pocket and squeezed through the fence, still not spotted by the teacher. Waiting for him was the friend who had called the warning.

"What'd you pick up out there, Kev?" the other boy asked.

For a moment Kevin said nothing. Part of him wanted to share his discovery – but another part wanted to keep it secret. He knew what might happen if others found out about his strange bug inside its almost magical metal case. Adults, he thought, would probably waste no time taking it away from him.

So he shrugged. "Nothing," he said to the other boy.

"Come on! I *saw* you! You picked up something shiny!"

Kevin thought quickly. "Oh, that," he said, trying to sound offhand. Fishing in his pocket, past the egg-shaped bit of mysterious metal, he brought out a leftover bit of his pocket money.

"Found a ten p," he said, holding it up.

"Lucky," the other boy said, not sounding very interested, and wandered off.

For the rest of the day, Kevin was lost in his imagination, dreaming daydreams about his discovery. He was growing more sure that the bug was very special. And he daydreamed about how the bug might turn out to be a tiny and friendly alien being of great intelligence and magical powers, who would be Kevin's secret friend and helper...

He was still full of such imaginings when he got home after school and hurried into his room for another private look at his discovery. But when the metal egg came open, easily, and the bug scuttled out, he was almost disappointed. It clearly did *not* behave like a woodlouse-sized version of E.T. It behaved just like any ordinary bug – scuttling around on its hairlike legs, waving its feelers, not doing much of anything.

But Kevin enjoyed playing with it. There seemed no danger that the bug would escape, for though it scuttled quite fast, it usually did so in short dashes. After each dash it would stop and wave its feelers, so that Kevin could easily gather it up.

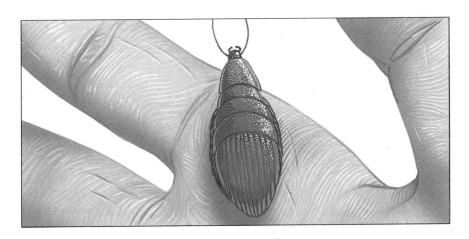

Then he noticed that his bug left a faint trail behind it, like a snail's slime trail but thinner and lighter. Kevin began to worry that his mother would see the trails and make a fuss. He also grew worried when the bug got over to the wall and climbed up – because for once it didn't stop after a short dash but went on climbing. Kevin had to get up on his table and then on to his chest of drawers before he could reach up and grab it.

And when he picked it off the wall, he saw a line of marks on the plaster, like tiny holes. As if the bug's slime trail had somehow eaten away small bits of the plaster, along the way.

So he put it back into its metal egg and decided it would be better to play with it outside where it wouldn't get him into any trouble.

The next day after school it rained. So Kevin left the bug in its case and spent some time trying to find out what kind of bug it was. But he had no luck. There were some picture books in his house about wildlife, even one that was all about insects – but nothing in any of the books looked at all like Kevin's bug.

Then he had another idea. That weekend he borrowed his father's Polaroid camera, which he had been shown how to use, and took a photograph of the bug – as close up as the camera could manage. Then on the Monday he took the photo to school, and showed it to Mr Cooper, a science teacher.

Mr Cooper seemed quite willing to help Kevin find out what some strange insect was called. But when he saw the photo, he just laughed.

"Oh, very good, Kevin," he said. "Part of it like a slug, part like a cockroach, legs like a millipede... What should we call it? A slug-roach-ipede?"

Kevin blinked. He was used to teachers saying weird things that they thought were funny, but he didn't understand why Mr Cooper was trying to be funny about the bug.

"If you made it yourself, you did a good job," Mr Cooper went on. "But it's just a bit too impossible. Or is it supposed to be a model of some alien monster?"

"No, it's ..." Kevin began. But then he stopped, deciding that it might be best not to tell Mr Cooper about the bug. Not if it was that strange. So he just smiled vaguely, took his photo back, and wandered away feeling puzzled and amazed.

He was still feeling that way some days later. After spending a lot of time he had seen hundreds of pictures of weird and gruesome insects, but not one of them looked anything like his bug – his slug-roach-ipede, as Mr Cooper had called it.

"I think you really are from space," Kevin told his bug the next afternoon. "So I suppose I'll never know what kind of bug you are."

He was sitting quietly among some low bushes at the side of his house, keeping out of sight of his mother who was gardening and his father who was washing the car.

20

The slug-roach-ipede was happily scuttling around on the bare earth, in its short breathless dashes.

"Maybe I should take you and show you to people at a TV station or something," Kevin told it. "I could get rich and

famous. The Boy who Found the Bug from Another World."

Then he got up quickly. The bug had started up the side of the house, and Kevin didn't want it to climb out of his reach. But it stopped after a short climb and sat still on the sun-warmed brick of the wall. Kevin saw that its head was moving in a strange way, just before he picked it off the wall.

Then he stared. Where the bug had been, a small round hole had appeared at the edge of one brick.

Frowning, Kevin put the bug back on to the wall. It scuttled a little way to the side, on to a very smooth brick. There it stopped, again with its head moving busily.

When Kevin lifted it away, he saw another, slightly larger hole in the smooth brick.

Kevin slid the bug back into the metal egg and sat thinking. He knew from the books that insects ate many different things. They ate leaves and fruit and flowers and each other. Some ate rotten meat, some ate wood, and he had even read of some that would eat rubber.

But he never had heard of a bug that ate bricks.

Or plaster – since he now had a good idea how his bug had made those small marks on the wall of his room.

It must be the only bug like it in the whole world, Kevin thought. I *will* be rich and famous. And he began to dream an enjoyable daydream of appearing with his bug as the star guests on "Blue Peter".

That was when his father found him and dragged him away to help with the car-washing. But he went on daydreaming all the rest of the weekend. And on the way to school on Monday he decided to tell some of his closest friends. Not that he wanted to boast or show off – not *really*. He just felt that his friends would be pleased to know how rich and famous he was going to be.

But at the morning break, he thought that he should have one more trial run – just to be sure the bug would perform, before anyone else saw it. So he slipped around the corner of the school, away from the main playground. Unseen for a moment, he took out the metal egg and released the bug on to the brick wall of the school.

It behaved just as he hoped. It scuttled upwards a little way, then stopped, its tiny head moving as it began to eat. Grinning to himself, Kevin reached for it.

But perhaps the bug had its meals interrupted by Kevin once too often. In any case, it scuttled away. And upwards, in an extra-long and high-speed dash.

A dash that took it high up the wall, out of Kevin's reach.

There it stopped, while Kevin vainly tried to jump up and grab it. And he hissed and chirped and whistled and did everything he could – without making too much noise and attracting attention – to try to get it to come down.

But it didn't. It climbed higher – towards something like a small run-off pipe, jutting out of the brick wall.

"No!" Kevin shouted, no longer caring if anyone heard. But the cry had no effect. The run-off pipe didn't fit all that tightly, and the bug managed to squeeze itself into the tiny space between the pipe and the bricks.

And it vanished. Into the wall of the school.

Kevin felt sick and miserable all the rest of that day. After school, he went back to the same place to look around, hoping that the bug had come out again. But there was no sign of it. Kevin knew that the wall with the run-off pipe was one wall of the school boiler room, which was always locked. But even so he went and stared through the window of the boiler room door. For a moment he thought he spotted the gleam of a slime trail, in one dim corner. But then the

caretaker came along, and Kevin fled.

For several days after that, Kevin went back to the boiler-room and peered in through that window. He also wandered around other parts of the school as well, looking for the slime trail of his lost bug, but the boiler room was his best hope. And it was there, finally, near the big boiler that heated the school, where he saw the sight that made him want to stay away from school.

It wasn't a slime trail. It was a *lot* of slime trails. Dozens of them, maybe hundreds, criss-crossing all over the floor and the brick walls of the boiler room. Along with dozens or

hundreds of small smooth holes, all over the walls.

Somehow, Kevin knew, the freedom and the warmth of the boiler room had caused his bug to give birth to a lot of littler bugs. Dozens, maybe hundreds, of baby slug-roach-ipedes. Who might soon themselves grow up and give birth to many more babies. *Hungry* ones.

If there was any doubt about it, the doubt vanished one

Monday morning soon afterwards. Everyone at school was talking about the weird vandals who had got into the school over the weekend and – for some reason – chopped away a large part of one brick wall in the gym.

It was a mystery why they had done that and nothing else, everyone said. It was also a mystery where the chopped-away bricks and mortar and brickdust had gone. And what the funny lines were, hundreds of them, all over the gym floor.

Kevin said nothing. He felt fairly sure that no one would believe him, then. And if people did come to believe him, later, they would *blame* him. Because he knew that something terrible was going to happen, and it was his fault.

He had let loose the bug that produced all the other bugs. Hundreds of them – maybe thousands or millions, before long – that all liked eating bricks. And that were loose in a building *made* of bricks.

Kevin was fairly sure that people would go on noticing the damage happening to the school walls. Teachers would keep the children out of school, when it started looking like the building might fall down. But Kevin was also sure – wretchedly, fearfully sure – that there was no way to stop that from happening.

He didn't even let himself *think* about what would happen if the bugs spread into the town, and the rest of the country, with all those brick buildings. It was bad enough to think about what was happening right there in his own school building.

No one would ever be able to catch or kill those small, scuttling, brick-eating bugs. Not even if they found out about them. The bugs would hide by day in the walls of the school building, and when it was empty after school they would come out, and eat and eat. Until one day there'd be ...

No more school.

Legend

Spring left the wood like a splinter
From a tree. Summer stared at the grass.
Autumn waited till the leaves dropped dead
Then it was winter, winter, nothing but winter.
Inside the wood a gloom of moss.
In its icy sky a red
Sun hung around like an eyesore till the moon
Took up night patrol and left at dawn.

Carrying haversacks and antique maps
Hunters headed for the wood to search
The naked branches and the frosted weeds
For clues, for secret places to set traps,
For clearings to see by fire and torch
What kept it cold. Their deeds
Added little to the local archives:
They found nothing and lost their lives.

Since then nobody has visited the wood,
Nor will the locals talk of it
Except to say that once some hunters went
To seek a purpose in the cold, made
Fires and set traps and used knives to cut
The trees, how something must have sent
Them to their deaths because they hear
Them cry in anguish each night of the year.

Alan Bold

26

The way through the woods

They shut the road through the woods
Seventy years ago.
Weather and rain have undone it again,
And now you would never know
There was once a road through the woods
Before they planted the trees.
It is underneath the coppice and heath,
And the thin anemones.
Only the keeper sees
That, where the ring-dove broods,
And the badgers roll at ease,
There was once a road through the woods.

Yet, if you enter the woods
Of a summer evening late,
When the night-air cools on the trout-ringed pools
Where the otter whistles his mate,
(They fear not men in the woods,
Because they see so few.)
You will hear the beat of a horse's feet,
And the swish of a skirt in the dew,
Steadily cantering through
The misty solitudes,
As though they perfectly knew
The old lost road through the woods...
But there is no road through the woods.

Rudyard Kipling

The green children

This text is taken from a report that was written in about 1150 by William of Newburgh.

In East Anglia there is a village, distant, as it is said, four or five miles from the noble monastery of the blessed king and martyr, Edmund; near this place are seen some very ancient cavities, called "Wolfpittes", that is, in English, "Pits for wolves", and which give their name to the adjacent village (Wulpet). During harvest, while the reapers were employed in gathering in the produce of the fields, two children, a boy and a girl, completely green in their persons, and clad in garments of strange colour, and unknown materials, emerged from these excavations. While wandering through the fields in astonishment, they were seized by the reapers, and conducted to the village, and many persons coming to see so novel a sight, they were kept some days without food.

But, when they were nearly exhausted with hunger, and yet could relish no species of support which was offered to them, it happened, that some beans were brought in from the field, which they immediately seized with avidity, and examined the stalk for the pulse, but not finding it in the hollow of the stalk, they wept bitterly. Upon this, one of the bystanders, taking the beans from the pods, offered them to the children, who seized them directly, and ate them with pleasure. By this food they were supported for many months, until they learned the use of bread. At length, by degrees, they changed their original colour, through the natural effect of our food, and become like ourselves, and also learned our language. It seemed fitting to certain discreet persons that they should receive the sacrament of baptism, which was administered accordingly.

The boy, who appeared to be the younger, surviving the baptism but a little time, died prematurely; his sister, however, continued in good health, and differed not in the least from the women of our own country. Afterwards, as it is reported, she was married at Lynne, and was living a few years since, at least, so they say. Moreover, after they had acquired our language, on being asked who and whence they were, they are said to have replied, "We are inhabitants of the land of St. Martin, who is regarded with peculiar veneration in the country which gave us birth." Being further asked where that land was, and how they came then hither, they answered, "We are ignorant of both those circumstances; we only remember this, that on a certain day, when we were feeding our father's flocks in the fields, we heard a great sound, such as we are now accustomed to hear at St. Edmund's when the bells are chiming; and whilst listening to the sound in admiration, we became on a sudden, as it were, entranced, and found ourselves among you in the fields where you were reaping." Being questioned whether in that land they believed in Christ, or whether the sun arose, they replied that the country was Christian, and possessed churches; but said they, "The sun does not rise upon our countrymen; our land is little cheered by its beams; we are contented with that twilight, which, among you, precedes the sunrise, or follows the sunset. Moreover, a certain luminous country is seen, not far distant from ours, and divided from it by a very considerable river." These, and many other matters, too numerous to particularize, they are said to have recounted to curious inquirers. Let every one say as he pleases, and reason on such matters according to his abilities; I feel no regret at having recorded an event so prodigious and miraculous.

The Iron Woman

In Lucy's attic bedroom it was still pitch black. But if she had been awake she would have heard a strange sound – a skylark singing high in the darkness above the house. And if she had been standing in the garden, and looking up into the dark sky through binoculars, she might have seen the glowing, flickering body of the lark, far up there, catching the first rays of the sun, that peered at the bird from behind the world.

The lark's song showered down over the dark, dewy fields, over the house roofs, and over the still, wet gardens. But in Lucy's bedroom it mingled with an even stranger sound, a strange, gasping whimper.

Lucy was having a nightmare. In her nightmare, somebody was climbing the creaky attic stair towards her. Then, a hand tried the latch. It was a stiff latch. To open the door, you had to pull the door towards you before you pressed the latch. If you didn't know the trick, it was almost impossible to open the door. The hand in Lucy's nightmare did not seem the know the trick. The latch clicked and rattled but stayed shut.

Then the latch gave a loud crack, and the door swung wide. On her pillow, Lucy became silent. She seemed to have stopped breathing.

For long seconds the bedroom was very dark, and completely silent, except for the faint singing of the skylark.

Then, in her dream, a hand was laid on Lucy's shoulder. She twisted her head and there, in her dream, saw a dreadful thing bending over her. At first, she thought it was a seal, staring at her with black, shining eyes. But how could it be a seal? It looked like a seal covered with black, shiny oil. A seal that had swum through an oil slick and climbed to her attic bedroom and now held her shoulder with its flipper.

But then she saw, on her shoulder, not a flipper but a human hand. And the hand, too, was slimed with black oil. Then Lucy suddenly knew this was not a seal but a girl, like herself, maybe a little bit younger. And the hand began to shake her, and the girl's face began to cry: "Wake up! Oh, wake up! Oh, please wake up!"

She cried those words so loud it was almost a scream, and Lucy did wake up.

She sat up in bed panting. What a horrible, peculiar dream. She pulled the bedclothes around her, and stared into the darkness towards the door. Was it open? She knew the door had been closed, as every night. But if the door was now open ...

At that moment, wide awake, she heard:

Tap, tap, tap.

On her window.

She listened, not daring to breathe, and it came again: *Tap, tap, tap.*

Was it a bird? An early bird? Sometimes little bluetits came and pecked at the putty around the edge of the window-panes, and peered in. But that was always during the day.

She slid out of bed and kneeled at the low window, parting the curtains.

At first, she couldn't see a thing. Just blackness. Then, pressing her nose to the glass, she made out the darker roof shapes of the house across the street. And then she noticed something very odd, close to the glass. Something quite small, and dimly white. As she peered, it came closer, till it almost touched the glass.

How could it be what it looked like?

She darted to switch her light on, beside her bed. She paused there, but only a moment, staring at her bedroom door, which was wide open. Then she went back to the window.

Very close to the glass, just outside the window, were three snowdrops. Their stalks were together, their heads hung apart.

How could three snowdrops be flying or floating outside an attic window, so high above the ground? She tugged the catch down, and opened the window.

The light shining from behind her made the darkness outside seem blacker than ever. But it lit the snowdrops, which were so close. And now she saw they were being held between a gigantic finger and thumb. They came towards her.

She jumped back, and half fell on to her bed. She lay there, staring at the open window. As she stared, the finger and thumb very daintily laid the three flowers on the sill, and withdrew.

32

Lucy was badly frightened. But, even more, she was curious and excited. Surely this was something wonderful. She must not be afraid. If she let herself be afraid now, what might she miss?

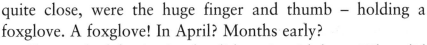

She went forward, and picked up the three flowers. They were real. But where could they be from? Snowdrops in April? Snowdrops were long past.

She peered out into the darkness. And there again, quite close, were the huge finger and thumb – holding a foxglove. A foxglove! In April? Months early?

She reached for it. As she did so, it withdrew. What did that mean? She thought: It wants me to follow. She remembered her nightmare, and the cry.

And now she could see a gigantic shape towering there in the darkness. It must be standing on their small garden, she thought. Or maybe out on the pavement.

She turned, and began to pull on her clothes.

Lucy eased open the front door and looked out. Her heart was pounding. What was she going to see? A person on top of a vehicle? Or on top of one of those cranes they use for repairing streetlights? Or simply a colossal person with those immense fingers? Whatever it was, the three snowdrops had been real enough. But the street was empty.

Now she was outside, the world seemed not quite so dark. Already, behind the roofs to the east, the inky sky had paled a little. She closed the door behind her and stood a moment, listening. She realized she was hearing a skylark, far up. Somewhere on the other side of the village a thrush sang a first few notes. But the great shape had vanished.

Then something brushed her face lightly and fell to the ground. She picked it up. A foxglove.

At the same moment, she smelt a dreadful, half-rotten smell. She knew it straightaway: the smell of the mud of the marsh. She thought it came from the foxglove. But no, it filled the whole air, and she looked upwards.

An immense dark head with two huge eyes was looking down at her, round the end of the house. It must be standing in the driveway, she thought, in front of the garage.

Lucy walked slowly round the end of the house, gazing up. And there it was. Not standing, but sitting – its back to the house wall. And here was the smell all right. This immense

creature seemed to be made entirely of black slime, with reeds and tendrils of roots clinging all over. Lucy simply stared up at the face that stared down at her. She felt a wild excitement, as if she were travelling at the most tremendous speed. Had this thing come from the sea, and waded through the marsh? She remembered the face like a seal's in her nightmare, the girl's face with eyes like a seal, and then very sharp and clear that voice crying: "Clean me." Had it said: "Clean me"? Was this what the snowdrops meant?

Lucy knew exactly what to do. She unrolled her father's hosepipe, which was already fitted to an outside tap, turned the tap full on, and pressed her finger half over the nozzle to make a stiff jet.

It was then she thought she heard another voice, a soft, rumbling voice. Like far-off thunder. She could not be sure where it came from. A strange voice. At least, it had a strange effect on Lucy. It made her feel safe and bold. And she seemed to hear:

"Waste no time."

The moment the jet hit the nearest leg she saw the bright gloss beneath. It looked like metal – polished black metal. The mud sluiced off easily. But it was a big job. And Lucy was thinking: What are people going to think when it gets light and they see this? She washed the nearest leg, the giant foot, the peculiar toes. She hosed between the toes. This first leg took about as much hosing as an entire car.

The voice came again, so low it seemed to vibrate inside her:

"Hurry!"

A faint tinge of pink outlined the chimneys to the east. Already it seemed that every single bird in the village must be singing. A van went past.

Lucy switched the jet to the face. It was an awesome face, like a great, black, wet mudpack. Then the giant hand opened palm upwards, flat on the driveway. Lucy saw what was wanted. She stepped on to the hand, which lifted her close to the face.

The jet sizzled into the deep crevices around the tightly closed eyes and over the strange curves of the cheeks. As she angled the jet to the massively folded shape of the lips, the eyes opened, brilliantly black, and beamed at her. Then Lucy saw that this huge being was a woman. It was exactly as if the rigid jet of water were carving this gleaming, black, giant woman out of a cliff of black clay. Last, she drove the slicing water into the hair – huge coils of wires in a complicated arrangement. And the great face closed its eyes and opened its mouth and laughed softly.

Lucy could see the muddy water splashing on to the white, pebble-dashed wall of the house and realized it was almost daylight. She turned, and saw a red-hot cinder of sun between two houses. A lorry thumped past. She knew then that she wasn't going to get this job finished.

At the same moment, still holding Lucy in her hand, the giant figure heaved upright. Lucy knew that the voice had rumbled, somewhere: "More water." She dropped the hose, which writhed itself into a comfortable position and went on squirting over the driveway.

"There's the canal," she said.

The other great hand pushed her gently, till she lay in the crook of the huge arm, like a small doll. This was no time to bother about the mud or the smell of it. She saw the light of her own bedroom go past, slightly below her, the window still open, as the giant woman turned up the street.

When they reached the canal, and stood on the bridge

looking down, Lucy suddenly felt guilty. For some reason, it was almost empty of water, as she had never seen it before. A long, black, oily puddle lay between slopes of drying grey mud. And embedded in the mud were rusty bicycle wheels, supermarket trolleys, bedsteads, prams, old refrigerators, washing machines, car batteries, even two or three old cars, along with hundreds of rusty, twisted odds and ends, tangles of wire, cans and bottles and plastic bags. They both stared for a while. Lucy felt she was seeing this place for the first time. It looked like a canal only when it was full of water. Now it was nearly empty, it was obviously a rubbish dump.

"The river," came the low, rumbling voice, vibrating Lucy's whole body where she lay.

The river ran behind a strip of woodland, a mile away across the fields. That was a strange ride for Lucy. The sun had risen and hung clear, a red ball. She could see a light on in a farmhouse. A flock of sheep and lambs poured wildly into a far corner. Any second she expected to hear a shout.

But they reached the strip of trees. And there was the river. It swirled past, cold and unfriendly in the early light. The hand set Lucy down among the weeds of the bank, and she watched amazed as the gigantic figure waded out into midstream, till the water bulged and bubbled past those thighs that were like the pillars of a bridge. There, in the middle of the river, the giant woman kneeled, bowed, and plunged under the surface. For a moment, a great mound of foaming water heaved up. Then the head and shoulders hoisted clear, glistening black, and plunged under again, like the launching of a ship. Waves slopped over the bank and soaked Lucy to the knees. For a few minutes, it was like a giant sea beast out there, rearing up and plunging back under, in a boiling of muddy water.

Then abruptly the huge woman levered herself upright and came ashore. All the mud had been washed from her body. She shone like black glass. But her great face seemed to writhe. As if in pain. She spat out water and a groan came rumbling from her.

"It's washed you," cried Lucy. "You're clean."

But the face went on trying to spit out water, even though it had no more water to spit.

"It burns!" Lucy heard. "It burns!" And the enormous jointed fingers, bunched into fists, rubbed and squeezed at her eyes.

Lucy could now see her clearly in full daylight. She gazed at the giant tubes of limbs, the millions of rivets, the funny concertinas at the joints. It was hard to believe what she was seeing.

"Are you a robot?" she cried.

Perhaps, she thought, somebody far off is controlling this creature, from a panel of dials. Perhaps she's a sort of human-shaped submarine. Perhaps ...

But the rumbling voice came up out of the ground, through Lucy's legs:

"I am not a robot," it said. "I am the real thing."

And now the face was looking at her. The huge eyes, huge black pupils, seemed to enclose Lucy – like the gentle grasp of a warm hand. The whole body was like a robot, but the face was somehow different. It was like some colossal metal statue's face, made of parts that slid over each other as they moved. Now the lips opened again, and Lucy almost closed her eyes, she almost shivered, in the peculiar vibration of the voice:

"I am Iron Woman."

I Believ

There IS a Loch Ness Mo
Yes, deep down in the wat

At times, when no one's watch
She'll part the water sur

And when she's really darin
She'll pluck up all her courag

40

nNessie

...er, I know that she exists.

...she lurks all turns and twists.

...and shove a great loop

...g, and she'll briefly come in view.

through.

she'll leave no room for doubt.

...nd poke her topknot out!

41

Secrets

One morning, at school, Rohan got every single sum wrong. Then he dropped a bottle of ink on the floor and it splashed on his teacher's white canvas shoes. When he made a face behind his teacher's back, he was seen. So he had to be punished.

"Here, take this letter to your father and go home," his teacher said, after writing a long and angry letter. "Let him punish you as well."

Rohan tried to look too proud to care, and picked up his books and walked out of the school yard and up the narrow city lane. But once he reached the big grey banyan tree that was the only tree in the lane, he found that the cobbler who usually sat under it, mending broken old shoes, was not there, he sat down in its shade, hiding himself in the folds of the great trunk, and sobbed a little with anger. He had not been able to get his sums right although he had tried. He had dropped the ink bottle by accident and not to spoil the teacher's white shoes. Perhaps it was bad of him to pull a face but how could he help it when things were going so badly? Now he was afraid to go home and hand the letter to his father, who would be very angry and beat him. He sometimes did, and often scolded him.

So Rohan hid there in the folds of the grey tree-trunk, and poked with a stick at the seeds dropped on the ground by the parrots that ate the red berries of the tree. He was so angry and afraid that he poked and poked with the stick till he had dug quite a deep hole in the  dust. In that hole he found a little grey lump of rubber – a plain piece of rubber that some other schoolboy might have dropped there long ago. He picked it up and rolled it about between his fingers.

"I wish it were a magic rubber," he said, sobbing a little, "I would rub out the whole school, like this – like this – " and he stepped out to look down the lane at the boys' school that stood at the end of it, and angrily rubbed at the air with the grey lump of rubber.

Then he stopped, his hand still in mid-air, his mouth still open, and his hair began to stand up on his head as it did on his neighbour's cat's back when she saw his dog.

Something very, very strange had happened. The school had vanished. He had really rubbed it out! The tall, three-storeyed house on its left, with its latticed balconies and green roof, was still there, and on the other side the tin-roofed warehouse where timber was stacked stood there too, but in between them, where the school had been, there was now a patch of earth. There was no white school building, no deep verandas, no dusty playground, no high grey wall and not a single schoolboy. There was just a square of bare brown earth between the other buildings, all quiet and still now in the heat of the afternoon.

Rohan's knees were shaking. He ran a little way down the road to see better but still could find nothing but a blank where the school had once been. Then he felt so afraid of the vanished school that he ran back up the lane as fast as he could, snatched up his books and the terrible rubber from among the roots of the banyan, and ran into the road where he lived. He hurried up the stairs at the side of the little yellow house to their room on the roof where his mother hung the clothes to dry and his father stacked old boxes and bicycle tyres.

His mother was alone at home. She was kneading dough in a big brass pan. The fire was not yet lit. "You're early," she said, in surprise. "I haven't any food ready for you yet. But you can go and break up an old box and get me some wood to light the fire. I'll warm some milk for you. Hurry up, don't look so sulky," she said, and began to roll and thump the dough in the pan, roll and thump, roll and thump, so she did not see the face Rohan made as he went out to pull an old crate to pieces and bring in an armload of packing-case wood.

He came in and threw it all into the grate with such force that the ashes and grit flew up and settled on all the pots and pans, and the dough and the neat floor as well.

His mother was so angry, she shouted, "What's the matter with you, you rascal? Look what you've done! What a mess you've made! Now go and fetch the broom and sweep it up at once."

"I won't sweep," he shouted back, as loudly as though there were a devil in him, shouting for him.

She was still more angry. "I won't sweep it up, either. Let it lie there and then your father will see it when he comes home," she said.

Then Rohan felt so afraid that he held up the magic rubber and cried, "I won't let you do that. I won't let him see it. I'll – I'll rub you all out," and he swept through the air with that little grey lump of rubber, as hard as he could. He shut his eyes tight because his face was all screwed up with anger, and when he opened them the whole house with the unlit fire, the brass pan, the glass of milk and even his mother had vanished. There was only the roof-top, blazing in the afternoon sun, littered with empty tins and old tyres at the edges but quite, quite bare in the middle.

Now Rohan did not have a home or a mother or even a glass of milk. His mouth hung open, he was so frightened by what he had done. Then he turned and ran down the stairs as fast as he could, so that his father would not come and find him standing alone on the empty roof-top.

He heard an excited bark and saw it was his dog Kalo, who had been sleeping in the shade of an overturned basket in a corner of the roof-top, but had heard him run down the stairs and followed him. Kalo was frightened, too, at the way their room had disappeared and the roof-top left standing empty, so was running along behind Rohan, barking with fright.

Rohan felt afraid that the people who lived in the yellow house would come out and see what had happened, so he shouted "Go back, Kalo! Go back!" But Kalo ran towards him, his long black ears flapping as he ran. So Rohan rubbed the air with his rubber again and screamed, "I don't want you! Go away!" and Kalo vanished. His round paw marks were still to be seen in the dust of the road. A little trail of dust was still hanging in the hot, still air of that dreadful afternoon, but Kalo the dog had vanished.

And someone had seen. An old man who traded in empty tins and bottles had just started his evening round and, while shouting "Tin and bo–" stopped short and stared till Rohan, rubbing in the air with his rubber again, shouted, "You can't see! You mustn't see!" and rubbed him out. That old man with his grey beard and big sack of clanking tins and bottles just disappeared as Kalo had.

Then Rohan turned and ran even faster. He ran into the big road that went round the mosque. Just in time he remembered that he might meet his father there, for he had a cycle repair shop at the foot of the mosque steps. So he whirled around

again. He kept going in circles, as if he were a little mad. At last he ran to the banyan tree, climbed over its roots into a cleft between two folds of the huge trunk and hid there, trembling.

"I'll hide this terrible rubber," he said at last. "I'll put it back in the hole and never, never take it out again." With shaking fingers he scraped more dust from the little hole he had dug earlier, in order to bury the rubber.

As he scraped and dug with trembling fingers, he found something else in the hole. At first he saw only one end of it – it was long and yellow. He dug harder and found it was a pencil. Quite a new pencil – he could see no one had used it before, though it looked old from being buried in the earth. He stopped crying and trembling as he wondered who could have buried a pencil here, and whether it was a magic pencil as the rubber was a magic one. He had to try it and see.

First he dropped the rubber into the hole and covered it up. Then he held up the pencil and pointed it at the bare patch of earth where the school had once stood between the warehouse and the green-roofed house. Very, very carefully he drew a picture of his old white school building in the air. He did it so carefully that he seemed to see the grey lines forming before his eyes. Then he blinked: the grey-white building really *was* there now. Or was it only a picture in his mind? Quickly he drew the verandas, the playground, the high wall, and then the little matchstick figures of a line of schoolboys rushing out of the front gate, the lane filling with them, and saw them leaping and running with their satchels flying behind them.

He stood up and ran a little way down the lane, out of the shade of the mysteriously whispering banyan tree. Now, in the clear sunlight, he could see the school quite plainly again, alive and noisy with children set free from their lessons. He stood there till he saw the teacher come out on his bicycle. Then he turned and ran the other way up the lane.

He stood in the middle of the dusty road and quickly, quickly, drew a picture of a little black dog in the air, as well as he could. He was still working on the long plumed tail when he heard Kalo bark, and saw him bounce down on to the road on his four feet and come pelting towards him.

As he came closer, Rohan saw he had missed out the jagged edge of Kalo's ear where it had been torn in a dog-fight. He was careful to add that so Kalo would be exactly as he had been before, scarred and dusty and wild with happiness. Kalo stood still, waiting for him to finish.

When it was done, he shouted, "Kalo! Kalo!" and patted him hastily, then went on busily with his pencil, drawing the old, bearded tin-and-bottle man. He was just drawing the big, bulging sack when he heard the cracked voice cry "-o-ttle

man!" and there he was, shuffling down the road and blinking a little in the bright light.

Then Rohan and his dog ran home, up the stairs to the empty roof-top. There, leaning against the low wall, his tongue between his teeth and his eyes narrowed, Rohan drew a picture of his home as well as he could. Even when he could see it quite plainly, the little whitewashed room with its arched windows and pigeon-roost on the flat roof, he went on drawing. He drew a picture of his mother kneading dough in a pan, the fire, the glass of milk and even the broom in the corner of the room. Then he went in and found them all there, just as he had drawn them. But he saw one mistake he had made in his drawing – he had coloured his mother's hair black and left out the grey strands over her ears. She had remained stiff, lifeless. He stood in the doorway, rubbing gently at the unnatural darkness of her hair till it showed the grey he knew. He realized you cannot draw a picture out of desperation, or with careless speed. It took care, attention, time.

When he had finished, his mother moved, looked up at him. "There's your milk," she said quietly, "drink it up."

He nodded. "I'll sweep up a bit first," he said, and went to fetch the broom. He swept and he swept, enjoying the work that he had not wanted to do at first, till he heard his father arrive, lean his bicycle against the wall and lock it, then come slowly up the stairs.

Rohan ran out, shouting, "Look, I found a pencil and a rubber on the road today." He wanted so much to tell his father all about it and ask him how it happened, but he did not dare.

His father was looking tired. "Why don't you sit quietly and draw something?" he said, as he went in for his tea.

Rohan nodded and went to fetch a piece of paper. Then he sat on the top step and spread out the paper and drew. He was not sure if the magic pencil would draw an ordinary picture. It did. Using it very, very carefully now, he drew a picture of Kalo.

When his father saw it, he beamed. He had never seen a picture as good. Rohan showed it to his mother too, and she was so pleased she pinned it on the wall, next to the calendar.

His father said, "I didn't know you could draw so well. Your teacher never told us. You should draw a picture for him."

Rohan spent the whole evening drawing with the magic pencil. He took the drawings to school next day, and his teacher was so pleased with them that he forgot to ask for an answer to his angry letter of the day before. He gave Rohan good paper and time to draw every day.

Rohan drew so much that the magic pencil was soon worn to a stub. Instead of throwing it away like an ordinary pencil, he took it down to the banyan tree and buried it in the earth at its roots where he had hidden the lump of rubber. As he walked away he worried about whether he would be able to draw as well with an ordinary pencil bought at the stationery shop near the school gate. But he had had so much practice now, and become so good an artist, that he found he could do as good a drawing with the new pencil he bought as with the magic one.

He became so famous in that town that people came from miles away to see the pictures his mother pinned to the walls of their house. They went to the school and asked the teacher about him. No one knew how he had learnt to draw and paint so well without any lessons or help. Even when he became a great artist, whose name was known all over the land, Rohan did not tell anyone the story. That was his secret – and the banyan tree's, and they kept it to themselves as secrets should be kept.

Pieces of eight

In Robert Louis Stevenson's famous novel, Treasure Island, *pirates, hidden treasure and the famous Long John Silver lead us from exciting adventure to new mysteries.*

Jim Hawkins has had a deadly fight with Long John Silver's pirates on the ship. He has been wounded, but is still alive. He realizes suddenly that he is alone. Have his ship mates made it safely to the nearby island?

I was now alone upon the ship; the tide had just turned. The sun was within so few degrees of setting that already the shadow of the pines upon the western shore began to reach right across the anchorage, and fall in patterns on the deck. The evening breeze had sprung up, and though it was well warded off by the hill with the two peaks upon the east, the cordage had begun to sing a little softly to itself and the idle sails to rattle to and fro.

I began to see a danger to the ship. The jibs I speedily doused and brought tumbling to the deck; but the mainsail was a harder matter. Of course, when the schooner canted over, the boom had swung out-board, and the cap of it and a foot or two of sail hung even under water. I thought this made it still more dangerous; yet the strain was so heavy that I half feared to meddle. At last, I got my knife and cut the halyards. The peak dropped instantly, a great belly of loose canvas floated broad upon the water; and since, pull as I liked, I could not budge the down-haul, that was the extent of what I could accomplish. For the rest, the *Hispaniola* must trust to luck, like myself.

By this time the whole anchorage had fallen into shadow – the last rays, I remember, falling through a glade of the wood, and shining bright as jewels, on the flowery mantle of the wreck. It began to be chill; the tide was rapidly fleeting seaward, the schooner settling more and more on her beamends.

I scrambled forward and looked over. It seemed shallow enough, and holding the cut hawser in both hands for a last security, I let myself drop softly overboard. The water scarcely reached my waist; the sand was firm and covered with ripple marks, and I waded ashore in great spirits, leaving the *Hispaniola* on her side, with her main-sail trailing wide upon the surface of the bay. About the same time the sun went fairly down, and the breeze whistled low in the dusk among the tossing pines.

At least, and at last, I was off the sea, nor had I returned thence empty-handed. There lay the schooner, clear at last from buccaneers and ready for our own men to board and get to sea again. I had nothing nearer my fancy than to get home to the stockade and boast of my achievements. Possibly I

might be blamed a bit for my truantry, but the recapture of the *Hispaniola* was a clenching answer, and I hoped that even Captain Smollett would confess I had not lost my time.

So thinking, and in famous spirits, I began to set my face homeward for the block-house and my companions. I remembered that the most easterly of the rivers which drain into Captain Kidd's anchorage ran from the two-peaked hill upon my left; and I bent my course in that direction that I might pass the stream while it was small. The wood was pretty open, and keeping along the lower spurs, I had soon turned the corner of that hill, and not long after waded to the mid-calf across the watercourse.

This brought me near to where I had encountered Ben Gunn, the maroon; and I walked more circumspectly, keeping an eye on every side. The dusk had come nigh hand completely, and, as I opened out the cleft between the two peaks, I became aware of a wavering glow against the sky, where, as I judged, the man of the island was cooking his supper before a roaring fire. And yet I wondered, in my heart, that he should now show himself so careless. For if I could see his radiance, might it not reach the eyes of Silver himself where he camped upon the shore among the marshes?

Gradually the night fell blacker; it was all I could do to guide myself even roughly towards my destination; the double hill behind me and the Spy-glass on my right hand loomed faint and fainter; the stars were few and pale; and in the low ground where I wandered I kept tripping among bushes and rolling into sandy pits.

Suddenly a kind of brightness fell about me. I looked up; a pale glimmer of moonbeams had alighted on the summit of the Spy-glass, and soon after I saw something broad and silvery moving low down behind the trees, and knew the moon had risen.

With this to help me, I passed rapidly over what remained to me of my journey; and, sometimes walking, sometimes running, impatiently drew near to the blockade. Yet, as I began to thread the grove that lies before it, I was not so thoughtless but that I slacked my pace and went a trifle warily. It would have been a poor end of my adventures to get shot down by my own party in mistake.

The moon was climbing higher and higher; its light began to fall here and there in masses through the more open districts of the wood; and right in front of me a glow of a different colour appeared among the trees. It was red and hot, and now and again it was a little darkened – as it were the embers of a bonfire smouldering.

For the life of me, I could not think what it might be.

At last I came right down upon the borders of the clearing. The western end was already steeped in moonshine; the rest, and the block-house itself, still lay in a black shadow, chequered with long, silvery streaks of light. On the other side of the house an immense fire had burned itself into clear embers and shed a steady, red reverberation, contrasted strongly with the mellow paleness of the moon. There was not a soul stirring, nor a sound beside the noises of the breeze.

I stopped, with much wonder in my heart, and perhaps a little terror also. It had not been our way to build great fires; we were, indeed, by the captain's orders, somewhat niggardly of firewood; and I began to fear that something had gone wrong while I was absent.

I stole round by the eastern end, keeping close in shadow, and at a convenient place, where the darkness was thickest, crossed the palisade.

To make assurance surer, I got upon my hands and knees, and crawled, without a sound, towards the corner of the house. As I drew nearer, my heart was suddenly and greatly lightened. It is not a pleasant noise in itself, and I have often complained of it at other times; but just then it was like music to hear my friends snoring together so loud and peaceful in their sleep. The sea cry of the watch, that beautiful "All's well", never fell more reassuringly on my ear.

In the meantime, there was no doubt of one thing; they kept an infamous bad watch. If it had been Silver and his lads that were now creeping in on them, not a soul would have seen daybreak. That was what it was, thought I, to have the captain wounded; and again I blamed myself sharply for leaving them in that danger with so few to mount guard.

By this time I had got to the door and stood up. All was dark within, so that I could distinguish nothing by the eye. As for sounds, there was the steady drone of the snorers, and a small occasional noise, a flickering or pecking that I could in no way account for.

With my arms before me I walked steadily in. I should lie down in my own place (I though, with a silent chuckle) and enjoy their faces when they found me in the morning.

My foot struck something yielding – it was a sleeper's leg; and he turned and groaned, but without awaking.

And then, all of a sudden, a shrill voice broke forth out of the darkness:

"Pieces of eight! Pieces of eight! Pieces of eight! Pieces of eight! Pieces of eight!" and so forth, without pause or change, like the clacking of a tiny mill.

Silver's green parrot, Captain Flint! It was she whom I had heard pecking at a piece of bark; it was she, keeping better watch than any human being, who thus announced my arrival with her wearisome refrain.

I had no time left me to recover. At the sharp, clipping tone of the parrot, the sleepers awoke and sprang up; and with a mighty oath, the voice of Silver cried:

"Who goes?"

I turned to run, struck violently against one person, recoiled, and ran full into the arms of a second, who, for his part, closed upon and held me tight.

"Bring a torch, Dick," said Silver, when my capture was thus assured.

And one of the men left the log-house and presently returned with a lighted brand.

Flannan Isle

"Though three men dwelt on Flannan Isle
To keep the lamp alight,
As we steered under the lee, we caught
No glimmer through the night."

A passing ship at dawn had brought
The news; and quickly we set sail,
To find out what strange thing might ail
The keepers of the deep-sea light.

The Winter day broke blue and bright,
With glancing sun and glancing spray,
While o'er the swell our boat made way,
As gallant as a gull in flight.

But as we neared the lonely Isle,
And looked up at the naked height,
And saw the lighthouse towering white,
With blinded lantern, that all night
Had never shot a spark
Of comfort through the dark,
So ghostly in the cold sunlight
It seemed, that we were struck the while
With wonder all too dread for words.

And as into the tiny creek
We stole beneath the hanging crag,
We saw three queer, black ugly birds –
Too big, by far, in my belief,
For cormorant or shag –
Like seamen sitting bolt-upright
Upon a half-tide reef:
But, as we neared, they plunged from sight,
Without a sound, or spurt of white.

And still too mazed to speak,
We landed; and made fast the boat;
And climbed the track in single file,
Each wishing he were safe afloat,
On any sea, however far,
So it be far from Flannan Isle:
And still we seemed to climb, and climb,
As though we'd lost all count of time,
Yet all too soon, we reached the door,
The black, sun-blistered lighthouse-door,
That gaped for us ajar.

As, on the threshold, for a spell,
We paused, we seemed to breathe the smell
Of limewash and of tar,
Familiar as our daily breath,
As though 'twere some strange scent of death:
And so, yet wondering, side by side,
We stood a moment, still tongue-tied:
And each with black foreboding eyed
The door, ere we should fling it wide,
To leave the sunlight for the gloom:
Till, plucking courage up, at last,
Hard on each other's heels we passed,
Into the living-room.

Yet, as we crowded through the door,
We only saw a table, spread
For dinner, meat and cheese and bread;
But, all untouched; and no one there:
As though, when they sat down to eat,
Ere they could even taste,
Alarm had come; and they in haste
Had risen and left the bread and meat:
For at the table-head a chair
Lay tumbled on the floor.

We listened; but we only heard
The feeble chirping of a bird
That starved upon its perch:
And, listening still, without a word,
We set about our hopeless search.

We hunted high, we hunted low;
And soon ransacked the empty house;
Then o'er the Island, to and fro,
We ranged, to listen and to look
In every cranny, cleft or nook
That might have hid a bird or mouse:
But, though we searched from shore to shore
We found no sign in any place:
And soon again stood face to face
Before the gaping door:
And stole into the room once more
As frightened children steal.
Ay: though we hunted high and low,
And hunted everywhere,
Of the three men's fate we found no trace

Of any kind in any place,
But a door ajar, and an untouched meal,
And an overtoppled chair.

As we listened in the gloom
Of that forsaken living-room –
A chill clutch on our breath –
We thought how ill-chance came to all
Who kept the Flannan Light:
And how the rock had been the death
Of many a likely lad:
How six had come to a sudden end,
And three had gone stark mad:
And one whom we'd all known as a friend
Had leapt from the lantern one still night,
And fallen dead by the lighthouse wall:
And long we thought
On the three we sought,
And of what might yet befall.

Like curs a glance has brought to heel,
We listened flinching there:
And looked, and looked, on the untouched meal,
And the overtoppled chair.

We seemed to stand for an endless while,
Though still no word was said,
Three men alive on Flannan Isle,
Who thought on three men dead.

Wilfred Wilson Gibson

Amy Johnson

On Monday, 5 May 1930, twenty-seven year old Amy Johnson was preparing to undertake her greatest challenge: to fly ten thousand miles, solo, to Australia. No woman had ever flown alone for so long a distance. Amy Johnson could not resist the challenge. She only had one hundred hours of flying experience, and many people believed that she would never make it to Australia.

Amy made her final checks on the engine of "Jason", her Gipsy Moth aeroplane, at Croydon aerodrome just outside London. The plane was second hand and had cost £600. It was a wooden biplane. Its wooden wings were covered with canvas. Inside the tiny wooden cockpit there were only a few instruments to help the pilot. Amy was a qualified pilot and ground engineer. If the plane needed any maintenance on the trip, she would have to do it herself!

Only a handful of people gathered to watch the little plane taxi unsteadily across the grass and take off. Shortly after 8pm, however, her dramatic encounters were being reported in the newspapers and international interest grew. For days, Amy had to fly through monsoon storms. The flimsy cockpit did not give her much protection and she could not see because of the rain. In Java she had to make a forced landing because the wings of the plane were damaged. She mended the tears in the wing fabric with sticking plaster!

On May 24, nineteen days after she had left London, Amy piloted "Jason" onto a landing strip in Darwin, northern Australia. She clambered to the ground jubilant at her success – she had broken the record for England to Australia. People were there to greet the dusty figure in khaki shorts and sun helmet. When Amy returned to Britain, she was awarded the CBE for her achievement.

Amy continued to be a record breaker. In 1931 she flew from England to Tokyo and back in record time. In 1936 she smashed the record for a flight to Cape Town in South Africa by doing the return trip in twelve days, fifteen hours. She married a well-known aviator, J.A. Mollinson, in 1933. Together, they flew another record breaking flight across the Atlantic from east to west in 39 hours.

At the outbreak of the Second World War, Amy joined the Air Transport Auxiliary. This was a group of civilians who used their skills to help the Royal Air Force. In the summer of 1940 she flew planes from the aircraft factories where they were made to air bases all over Britain. On the 6th January, 1941, observers noticed a plane in difficulties over the Thames estuary. The pilot was Amy Johnson. The plane faltered, and then suddenly fell from the sky, spiralled down and plunged into the sea a few miles away. Small boats made their way to the wreckage floating on the water, but they found no sign of Amy.

Amy Johnson's last flight remained a mystery. No one could understand why such an experienced and courageous pilot met with difficulty on this routine flight. People were certain, however, that Amy Johnson was an international heroine with many admirers. She is still remembered today as the best-known female aviator of those days, as well as for her courage and determination.

TIMETABLE:

1903	Born in Hull, Yorkshire, to a fish merchant's family
1925	Graduates from Sheffield University with a degree in economics
1928	Takes up flying and qualifies as a pilot and ground engineer
1930	Flies to Australia solo, and breaks the record for this 10,000 mile flight
1931	Flies from England to Tokyo and back in record time
1933	Marries J.A. Mollinson, the well-known aviator
1936	Flies from Cape Town, South Africa to England in record time
1941	Dies when her plane crashes into the sea near the Thames Estuary

THE ILLUSTRATED
LONDON NEWS

SATURDAY MAY 31, 1930

The success of Miss Amy Johnson's magnificent solo flight from London to Australia was largely due, no doubt, to her expert technical skill. She is the only woman who holds an Air Ministry certificate as a ground engineer, and at each halt during her flight her first care was to overhaul her engine. It is a standard Gipsy Moth machine, with one engine of 100 h.p. When she landed at Port Darwin on May 24 (Empire Day) she was accorded a great reception and received some 500 telegrams of congratulation, including those from the King, the Prime Minister, the Secretary for Air, and the Premier of Australia, who invited her to Canberra. She left Port Darwin on May 26 to resume her flight towards Sydney. Although she took twenty days to reach Australia, against Squadron-Leader Hinker's 15½ days in 1928, she was two days ahead of his time as far as Rangoon, and made a record for a solo flight to India in six days.

Miss Amy Johnson, who left Croydon Aerodrome on May 5, landed at Port Darwin, Australia, on Empire Day, May 24. This great feat has captured the imagination of the world.

She is a daughter of Mr and Mrs J.W. Johnson, of Hull, and is a BA of the University of Sheffield. From Port Darwin she flew to Daly Waters (320 miles) and from thence to Alexandra Station (200 miles), and Cloncurry, Queensland, arranging to leave for Brisbane (600 miles further) on the 27th. The De Havilland "Gipsy Moth" light aeroplane in which she made her flight is of the type that anyone can acquire today for £595. The "Moth" is being used by hundreds of owner-pilots and commercial operators everywhere, and it is the standard equipment of the great majority of Flying Clubs and schools throughout the world.

When Miss Johnson bought her second-hand "Moth" it had already flown 35,000 miles. Now, after her Australian flight, the machine, with its original engine, has flown about 50,000 miles. Its wonderful engine is a De Havilland 100 h.p. "Gipsy One", air-cooled, with overhead valves. Maintenance is simplified as water-cooling complications do not exist.

Nearly 10,000 miles in nineteen days: a table of Miss Johnson's flight from Croydon to Port Darwin, with her halting-places and mileage

DAY		MILES
1	Vienna	780
2	Constantinople	790
3	Aleppo	550
4	Baghdad	470
5	Bandar Abbas	830
6	Karachi	720
7	Jhansi	720
8	Allahabad	230
8	Calcutta	460
9	Insein	650
10 & 11	Held up for repairs	
12	Bangkok (Siam)	355
13	Singora	500
14	Singapore	470
15	Tjomal	700
16	Samarang	120
17	Surabaya	200
18	Atamboea	459
19	Port Darwin	500
	TOTAL	9495

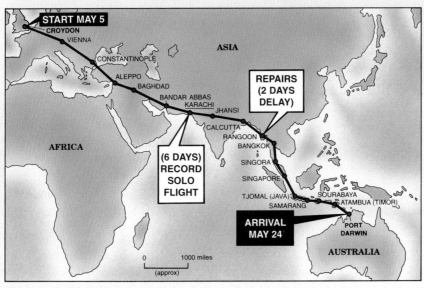

67

The elephant poachers

The author of this extract has used real places and true facts about elephant poaching in Kenya, for the background of her story. Kiprono has lived in Kenya all his life and knows much about elephants and the way they live. In this extract, he tries to find the hideout of a gang of elephant poachers.

Kimri and Peyo-Peyo went to bed, Merlin stayed a while by the fire, listening to the crackling silence of the night: it was like thin ice, he thought, you couldn't see the swirling life beneath it. Only the raucous cry of a bush-baby, then the hysterical cackle of a hyena telling you that the stillness was one huge hoax of Nature. No, he thought. Telling you that what you see and feel and hear is only one fraction of what you don't. He walked over to his tent. About to unzip the flap, he glanced up. Elephants were passing behind the tents, seven of them and a baby. Moving with uncanny silence, they passed through the silver skein of the bush in single file; then sailed out of the trees into the moonlight, great grey shadows gliding towards their secret destination. Suddenly he was certain it was the herd that frequented the forest behind the bamboo fence. He called his special call. They stopped. The matriarch trumpeted. Then they surrounded him, and she touched him gently with her trunk. After a while, they continued silently on through the moonlight.

A few hours later, just before dawn, he awoke to the sound of distant gun shots. First one, then another and another.

Kiprono too had heard the reports of the gun.

Tracking the poachers had been easy, as clear to him as footprints in a clean stretch of sand. Besides, there were several of them, and that helped as well.

Eventually he found himself cutting through the bush in the direction of the sound in order to eliminate the twists and turns of the path. Night began to fall, and he picked berries to ease his hunger. Then, cutting a pointed stick with his knife, he dug till he reached the roots of a certain tree; as always, they yielded water. His progress slowed down by darkness, he had tunnelled a small den in the bushes, cut himself a bed of dry grass, and used more of the long strawlike stems as a cover. At day-break he had continued on, following the tracks until he was almost half-way to Maximillian's. Suddenly he had stopped. There was a light breeze and it brought to his sensitive nostrils a smell that he recognized immediately: it was the strong smell of men who lived in the bush, of men whose sweat was tainted with the acrid scent of fear, and cunning, and brutality. He lay down, put his ear to the ground and caught the vibration of steps: they were coming towards him.

He hid behind the nearest rock. Now he heard the murmur of voices; then the crackle of a twig. Within minutes he saw them. Five men. They were carrying two elephant tusks. They seemed to be coming straight towards the rock, and his heart beat wildly. They veered a little to the right, and he slid round the left end of the rock. It was high and jagged, like a miniature mountain. Breath inheld, rigid with fear, pressed hard against the rock as though to make himself a part of it, he heard them walk past. Then they disappeared. Crouching low, he ran to the next bush. There was only one thought in his mind: he must follow them until they reached their hiding place. Almost certainly they had a cache of ivory there. And they would stop at this place, and bury the tusks they were carrying. Eventually a vehicle would come and carry the tusks away. He had to find out where their hideout was, then get back to the farm as fast as he could and bring Merlin and Ol-le-Langoi here with him to catch them. They were moving in the direction of the farm; the closer they went the quicker he'd get back.

He ran to the next bush. Startled, a black-plumed ostrich raced ahead of him on skittery legs. He froze to the ground, thinking the men might turn and see him. But they saw only the ostrich and continued on. The bushes were quite thick here, and it was growing dark. He could still see the men clearly though, and now they sat down to rest; he wondered how far they had come, and scorned them for their lack of stamina. After a while they continued on. This time they did not stop until the small hours.

The moon was bright, and it was easy to keep track of them. And now he saw they were making towards a craggy mass of rock; it was taller than four men, he thought, and wide as it was high. Four of them disappeared around one end of the rock. The fifth kept guard. He could hear the sound of boulders being dragged away; then digging. And he knew that they were burying the tusks. He glanced round him, took his bearings so that there would be no difficulty in finding this spot when he returned with Merlin. Bending low, he started to move away to the left of the rock. At the moment when he thought it was safe to straighten up and begin to run, he felt another presence. Felt it and smelt it.

It was a lone elephant with a small calf.

He retraced his steps, and soon he saw them. They were approaching the poachers' hideout.

His mind raced, his small, wiry body quivered, thoughts whirled wildly. How could he head them away from death? A plan leapt into his head. He would run to the right end of the rock, then begin to yell when he was sufficiently far from it to give him a lead. The poachers would follow, but he knew certainly he could outstrip them. And the elephant and her calf would veer away from the turmoil.

Keeping as low as he could without impeding his speed, he

took off; ran back towards the right end of the rock, then ran past it. After a couple of minutes he began to yell at the top of his voice. He heard the poachers charging after him, scattering their numbers so that there was a better chance of finding him. He ran on, stopped at a tree deep in shadow; climbed it. Two of the poachers ran past. He waited breathlessly. But he knew they would never leave their cache unguarded for long. And they would always vanish rather than fight.

After a while, all was still. It seemed to him ominously still. He climbed down the tree, stood motionless and concentrated deep within himself as his people did when they wanted to understand a message carried to them by the beat of drums. He knew all was not well, but he could not define it. He ran towards the farm, keeping a steady loping pace that he could maintain for long distances.

It was a half hour later, just before dawn, that he heard the report of a gun. First one, then another and another.

The voices of silence

For years, the Berlin Wall divided communist East Germany from the capitalist west. This story is set in 1989, when the wall was torn down.

Flora lives in Romania, under the régime of President Ceauşescu. When the Wall came down, she sensed the tension rising. Before long she begins to realize that something is happening to her father.

When I got home from school Tata was there already, which was unusual. He jumped guiltily, and pushed a book back into the crowded, rickety shelf unit, as if caught out doing something wrong.

"Why are you here so early?" I asked.

"We were sent home – production stopped because of the electricity," he said.

I hit the switch, but of course nothing happened. The room was full of the darkening grey of a November afternoon, damp and chill. Out of habit I went through to the kitchen and came back with two candleholders which I set up ready, although we wouldn't light them until absolutely necessary, because of the extravagance. I sighed. Doing my homework by candlelight was a strain. But maybe the lights would go back on soon.

"I'm going out, Flora," said Tata. "Your mother asked me to try to get some fruit, and I heard there might be some at the back of the supermarket. OK?"

I nodded. It didn't worry me to be left alone, even on such a dreary, dwindling day. Mama always used to tell me when I was little that only foolish children were afraid of ghosts and goblins and things that make noises in the night. "It's the real people you have to be afraid of," she would say.

As soon as the door closed behind my father I rushed over to the shelf unit, to see what book he had been looking at. Was it fat, or thin? Blue, or red? I couldn't remember. So I pulled out a volume of folk tales and flicked through it – then thought. It had been on that shelf, I was sure. Next to the tales was the one book in the house you can be sure he wouldn't have looked at – a volume of Ceaușescu's speeches. We had it because ... well, you had to have such things. Just in case.

Something made me take out the fat book. On the jacket was a highly coloured photograph of our President, taken at least twenty years earlier, so that this eternally young, impossibly rosy-cheeked man beamed out at me. I opened the pages in the middle, and then nearly dropped the book in shock. Because someone had cut out the pages to make a secret compartment, and there, hidden in the centre of Ceaușescu's interminable speeches was ... money. I had never seen such money. There were green dollars in little rolls, and brightly-coloured Deutschmarks. American and German banknotes ... hard currency, we called it, what everyone dreamt of, and what some men would kill their grandmothers to obtain. Our own money, the grubby *lei*, was worthless. To

deal on the black market, to get American cigarettes, to bribe people, you needed hard currency. And here it was – hidden in my own home. It looked like a fortune. But what was it doing there? How long had he been collecting it – and *how*? Did Mama know?

The evening seemed to pass very slowly. It should have been happy. The electricity went back on. Mama had managed to find a bit of chicken, which she made into a stew, with potato and onion and cabbage. It was the most delicious meal we had had in a long time, and yet I could barely taste it. I kept glancing at my father, and thinking of that mutilated book just across the room. It was as if a silent monster was crouched on the shelf, waiting to devour us all.

I couldn't wait to retreat to my room, although Mama asked me if I felt ill. She could tell something was wrong.

"I've got a sore throat," I lied, wanting to escape from them.

When my light was out I tried to sleep, but the vision of that currency kept dancing in front of my eyes in the darkness, mocking me with my lack of understanding. What was he saving for? It couldn't possibly be for Christmas.

I must have dozed off, because when I woke the room seemed much colder. I glanced across to the wall, and indeed the little flame of my own paraffin heater had been turned off, as usual. One of them must have crept in.

But they hadn't gone to bed. As usual, I could hear the radio, playing folk music. Behind it, they were talking, in those controlled intense tones they always used for a row. Yet this wasn't a row; their voices weren't angry. Even though I couldn't make out the words I could tell the discussion was serious, as if words were being weighed very carefully before being dropped into the pool. My mind full of that hidden money and all that had happened during the day, I knew I had to hear.

Careful not to make my bed creak, I got up. It took me a long time to lower the handle of my door, and inch it open, and creep out into the hall. My bare feet made no sound on the icy linoleum. I was in luck – the living room was open just a crack.

"You understand now, Rodi," he said.

"I ... well ... we've been through it so often it's a relief to have come to a decision," said Mama, with a big sigh. "I did think, when the news came from Germany, that you'd wait. I thought things might change here. You thought it too, at first ..."

He broke in. "Rodika, my darling! We've got to be realistic. You *know* we're different. The Czechs, the Poles – they've always had it easy, compared to us. This place will never change. That's why I got so depressed. All the good news just rubbed my nose in our own situation. When the old Cobbler dies there's two equally bad sons to take his place. So what hope is there?"

"None," she said. And her voice was so sad and low it made me want to cry.

"So – I've got no choice, Rodi. Please understand. I have to do it," he said, in a low, pleading voice.

"What if you ...?" she began.

"I won't. It'll work, I promise you!"

"They shoot people," she cried.

"No," he said. "I'll make it."

"Then what? How long will it be?"

"Oh Rodi – how can I know? But you'll apply to join me,

you and Flora, and in time they'll let you. They have to. It may be hard – but I believe this is the only chance for a better life for all of us."

I could see them through the door. They both got up, and enveloped each other in a massive hug before breaking apart and carrying on talking, still with their arms around each other.

"I can take it, Constantin – for your sake."

"For all our sakes," he said.

"But you're the one who's going," she said wistfully. "And if anything goes wrong, we'll be the ones left here."

"I know," he said.

"When ..." her voice faltered again. "When will it happen?"

"Not for a while. The colder it is the better. Mircea and Stefan know the route, and they say the border guards there skive off on the coldest nights. Anyway, now I've got your backing I can carry on planning."

"Did you need my permission, my love?" asked Mama, in a sad, faraway voice, as if she had long given up the struggle.

"I need you to believe in me," said Tata.

And they clung to each other again, as if all the soldiers and secret police in the world would not be able to break them apart. I heard the muffled words, "I love you," but I couldn't see anything any more. Blindly I backed away, and I don't know how I got back to my bedroom without them hearing me. But then, they were too involved in their own drama to think about me.

Lying in my bed in the pitch darkness, I felt as if I was tossing in a tiny boat on some vast, black ocean. There was nothing around me any more, nothing to keep me safe, only the howling of the wind and the beating of the rain. And the rain was the tears which poured down my cheeks, whilst my secret, silent voice howled out a long cry of pain. At last I knew what it all meant.

He was getting the currency from somewhere, and making plans with his friends to cross the border. He would go, and Mama and I would be left behind. Maybe we would never see him again, but that was a price he was obviously prepared to pay – and she was letting him.

My father was going to leave us.

Geography lesson

When the jet sprang into the sky,
it was clear why the city
had developed the way it had,
seeing it scaled six inches to the mile.
There seemed an inevitability
about what on ground had looked haphazard,
unplanned and without style
when the jet sprang into the sky.

When the jet reached ten thousand feet,
it was clear why the country
had cities where rivers ran
and why the valleys were populated.
The logic of geography –
that land and water attracted man –
was clearly delineated
when the jet reached ten thousand feet.

When the jet rose six miles high,
it was clear that the earth was round
and that it had more sea than land.
But it was difficult to understand
that the men on the earth found
causes to hate each other, to build
walls across cities and to kill.
From that height, it was not clear why.

Zulfikar Ghose